A Kodansha Comics Trade Paperback Original
Attack on Titan 34 copyright © 2021 Hajime Isayama
English translation copyright © 2021 Hajime Isayama

All rights reserved.

Published in the United States by Kodansha Comics, an imprint of Kodansha USA Publishing, LLC, New York.

Publication rights for this English edition arranged through Kodansha Ltd., Tokyo.

First published in Japan in 2021 by Kodansha Ltd., Tokyo as *Shingeki no kyojin*, volume 34.

Standard Edition
ISBN 978-1-64651-236-2

Barnes & Noble Edition
ISBN 978-1-64651-459-5

BAM Edition
ISBN 978-1-64651-460-1

Kinokuniya Edition
ISBN 978-1-64651-461-8

Original cover design by Takashi Shimoyama/Manami Fukunaga (Red Rooster)

Printed in the United States of America.

www.kodansha.us

9 8 7 6 5 4 3 2 1
Translation: Ko Ransom
Lettering: Dezi Sienty
Editing: Tiff Joshua TJ Ferentini, Ben Applegate
Kodansha Comics edition cover design by Phil Balsman

Publisher: Kiichiro Sugawara

Director of publishing services: Ben Applegate
Associate director of operations: Stephen Pakula
Publishing services managing editors: Alanna Ruse, Madison Salters
Production managers: Emi Lotto, Angela Zurlo

Young characters and steampunk setting, like *Howl's Moving Castle* and *Battle Angel Alita*

Beyond the Clouds © 2018 Nicke / Ki-oon

A boy with a talent for machines and a mysterious girl whose wings he's fixed will take you beyond the clouds! In the tradition of the high-flying, resonant adventure stories of Studio Ghibli comes a gorgeous tale about the longing of young hearts for adventure and friendship!

THE SWEET SCENT OF LOVE IS IN THE AIR! FOR FANS OF OFFBEAT ROMANCES LIKE *WOTAKOI*

Sweat and Soap © Kintetsu Yamada / Kodansha Ltd.

In an office romance, there's a fine line between sexy and awkward... and that line is where Asako — a woman who sweats copiously — meets Koutarou — a perfume developer who can't get enough of Asako's, er, scent. Don't miss a romcom manga like no other!

KC
KODANSHA
COMICS

PERFECT WORLD
Rie Aruga

A TOUCHING NEW SERIES ABOUT LOVE AND COPING WITH DISABILITY

An office party reunites Tsugumi with her high school crush Itsuki. He's realized his dream of becoming an architect, but along the way, he experienced a spinal injury that put him in a wheelchair. Now Tsugumi's rekindled feelings will butt up against prejudices she never considered — and Itsuki will have to decide if he's ready to let someone into his heart...

"Depicts with great delicacy and courage the difficulties some with disabilities experience getting involved in romantic relationships... Rie Aruga refuses to romanticize, pushing her heroine to face the reality of disability. She invites her readers to the same tasks of empathy, knowledge and recognition."
—Slate.fr

"An important entry [in manga romance]... The emotional core of both plot and characters indicates thoughtfulness... [Aruga's] research is readily apparent in the text and artwork, making this feel like a real story."
—Anime News Network

Knight of the ICE

Yayoi Ogawa

Knight of the Ice ©Yayoi Oga...

SKATING THRILLS AND ICY CHILLS WITH THIS NEW TINGLY ROMANCE SERIES!

A rom-com on ice, perfect for fans of *Princess Jellyfish* and *Wotakoi*. Kokoro is the talk of the figure-skating world, winning trophies and hearts. But little do they know... he's actually a huge nerd! From the beloved creator of *You're My Pet* (*Tramps Like Us*).

Chitose is a serious young woman, working for the health magazine *SASSO*. Or at least, she would be, if she wasn't constantly getting distracted by her childhood friend, international figure skating star Kokoro Kijinami! In the public eye and on the ice, Kokoro is a gallant, flawless knight, but behind his glittery costumes and breathtaking spins lies a secret: He's actually a hopelessly romantic otaku, who can only land his quad jumps when Chitose is on hand to recite a spell from his favorite magical girl anime!

KC
KODANSHA
COMICS

A SMART, NEW ROMANTIC COMEDY FOR FANS OF *SHORTCAKE CAKE* AND *TERRACE HOUSE!*

A romance manga starring high school girl Meeko, who learns to live on her own in a boarding house whose living room is home to the odd (but handsome) Matsunaga-san. She begins to adjust to her new life away from her parents, but Meeko soon learns that no matter how far away from home she is, she's still a young girl at heart — especially when she finds herself falling for Matsunaga-san.

THANK YOU FOR READING!

ATTACK ON SCHOOL CASTES

WELL...

HOW'D YOU LIKE THE LAST EPISODE?

HM.

IT'S ALL OVER...

MAKES SENSE, YOU DON'T READ THE FANSITES.

OH...

THE CHARACTERS GOT A PROPER SEND-OFF TOO, SO...

IT WAS A REALLY LONG STORY... BUT ALL THE FORESHADOWING REALLY PAID OFF.

I THOUGHT IT WAS GOOD.

DIDN'T YOU WANT THEM TO SUBVERT YOUR EXPECTATIONS, BUT, YOU KNOW, IN A **GOOD** WAY?!

IT'S EXACTLY WHAT I THOUGHT IT'D BE!!

SORRY TO SAY...

AND I'D PREDICTED THE ENDING TO THIS SERIES OVER TEN YEARS AGO...

THERE WERE SO MANY LOOSE ENDS!

...I'M SORRY, SYMPATHIZER TO THE DARK, BUT YOUR VOICE IS TOO QUIET FOR ME TO HEAR...

Attack on Titan
·The End·

EREN ...

EVERYONE WILL BE COMING TO VISIT YOU SOON.

ISN'T THAT NICE?

LET'S
TELL
THEM
EVERY-
THING...

...ABOUT OUR STORY.

WHY THOSE WHO TRIED TO KILL ONE ANOTHER FOR SO LONG...

...HAVE APPEARED ON PARADIS... TO ADVOCATE FOR PEACE.

THEY'LL WANT TO KNOW WHAT WE SAW.

DO YOU REALLY THINK THIS IS GOING TO WORK...?

... ARMIN.

PARADIS IS WITHIN SIGHT NOW.

WE KILLED EREN, A MAN REVERED BY THE PEOPLE OF ELDIA...

AND WE'RE THE ALLIED NATIONS' AMBASSADORS FOR PEACE TALKS...?

WE DESTROYED THE WALLS.

WE BETRAYED THE ISLAND.

I KNOW SHE'LL DEFEND US, TOO.

HER MAJESTY'S FIRST MOVE WAS TO PROTECT JEAN'S RELATIVES AND MY MOM...

BELIEVE IN HISTORIA.

PERSONALLY... I WOULDN'T BE SHOCKED IF THEY SANK OUR SHIP RIGHT HERE.

...THEY'LL HAVE TO WANT TO HEAR...

BUT... WHEN THEY SEE US ALL TOGETHER LIKE THIS...

ANNIE... CONFLICT WILL NEVER VANISH.

US WEAK LITTLE THINGS...

IN A WORLD WITHOUT TITANS.

HOW MANY TIMES DO I HAVE TO TELL YOU TO NOT LUST AFTER A MARRIED WOMAN? CREEP.

...I NEVER GET TIRED OF HISTORIA'S BEAUTIFUL HANDWRITING. IT EVEN SMELLS NICE.

DON'T YOU MEAN THE FIELD GUIDE TO HORSES?

...FOR ALL THE GIRLS WHO EVER OPEN A HISTORY TEXTBOOK.

TRYING TO LOOK GOOD FOR SOME- ONE?

YOU SEEM AWFULLY CONCERNED ABOUT HOW YOUR HAIR LOOKS YOUR- SELF, JEAN.

IT'S A DAMN SHAME YOU GOT A NEW LEASE ON LIFE, REINER.

THIS FIGHT WILL NOT END UNTIL EITHER ELDIA OR THE WORLD DISAPPEARS.

THAT IS WHAT EREN SAID, AND PERHAPS HE WAS RIGHT AFTER ALL.

EVEN SO, HE CHOSE TO LEAVE THIS WORLD IN OUR HANDS.

AND WE ARE ALIVE, NOW.

THOSE WHO SURVIVED AFTER AN UNFATHOMABLE NUMBER OF LIVES WERE TAKEN ARE STILL TORMENTED BY UNHEALING SCARS.

THE NATION OF ELDIA HAS FORMED A SO-CALLED ARMY CONTROLLED BY THE YEAGERISTS, WHO NOW FOCUS THEIR EFFORTS ON BUILDING THEIR MILITARY STRENGTH.

AS THE WORLD SUFFERS THROUGH THIS LOSS, THEIR FEARS HAVE COME TRUE.

...THE ISLAND CRIES OUT AS ONE.

FEARFUL OF RETALIATION FROM WHAT IS LEFT OF HUMANITY ON THE OTHER SIDE OF THE SEA...

THREE YEARS
HAVE PASSED
SINCE THE DAY
KNOWN AS
**THE BATTLE
OF HEAVEN
AND EARTH.**

...IS THAT SO?

THAT'S... WONDERFUL.

I GUESS I'M NOT THE ARMORED TITAN ANYMORE...

MOM... I...

THIS IS ALL... I EVER NEEDED.

I'M SORRY... FOR EVERYTHING.

HUH?

REINER...

HEALED UP ALREADY ...?

ANNIE ...?

HUH ...?

I DON'T KNOW WHAT WILL HAPPEN AFTER I DIE...

BUT I KNOW...

...YOU CAN MAKE IT TO THE OTHER SIDE OF THE WALLS.

HUMANITY WILL BE SAVED...

...BY YOU...

...ARMIN.

YOU'LL PROBABLY REMEMBER THIS AGAIN ONCE IT'S ALL OVER...

BUT...

NEXT TIME WE MEET, WE'LL BE TRYING TO KILL ONE ANOTHER.

THANK YOU.

...EREN.

I SWEAR I WON'T LET THIS TERRIBLE MISTAKE YOU'RE MAKING BE IN VAIN.

YOU BE-CAME...

...A MASS MURDERER FOR OUR SAKE...

...WHY?

I WANTED... TO LEAVE EVERY SURFACE A BLANK PLAIN...

...AND LEAVE THE LAND COVERED IN CARRION-FATTENED INSECTS A FEW DAYS LATER.

LEVEL ALMOST EVERY FOREST...

...I THINK I STILL WOULD HAVE FLATTENED THIS WORLD.

EVEN IF I DIDN'T KNOW THAT YOU'D STOP ME IN THE END...

I DON'T REMEMBER EVER FORGIVING YOU!

WHAT? **WHO KNOWS** ?!

... OW!

A WOMAN WHO'S ALWAYS VALUED YOU OVER EVERYTHING, EVEN HER OWN LIFE!

WHAT ARE YOU THINKING, DISREGARDING MIKASA'S LOVE FOR YOU LIKE THAT?!

DO YOU REALLY THINK YOU CAN TELL HER TO FORGET ABOUT YOU AND BE DONE WITH IT?!

ON THE OTHER HAND... MAYBE SHE'LL FIND SOMEONE PERFECT FOR HER IN NO TIME...

SHE SHOULD BE ABLE TO FORGET ABOUT THE HEARTBREAKER SHE LOVED AND BE HAPPY AT THE VERY LEAST!

SO.

WHAT WERE YOU THINK-ING?

ABOUT WHAT?

ABOUT MIKASA.

DO YOU THINK SHE CAN JUST FORGET ABOUT YOU AND LIVE A HAPPY LIFE WITH SOMEONE ELSE?

...WELL.

JUST LIKE YOU WANTED...?

WHO KNOWS.

LET'S GO...

...EREN.

...YEAH.

...I MOVED FORWARD.

THAT'S WHY...

ALL OF IT... HAS BEEN TO ARRIVE AT THAT RESULT.

...IS THE RESULT OF MIKASA'S CHOICE.

THE ONLY THING I KNOW FOR SURE...

...WRAPPED UP IN THIS BATTLE, WITHOUT EVEN KNOWING IF YOU'D SURVIVE IT.

GETTING EVEN MY PRECIOUS FRIENDS...

FORCING YOU TO FIGHT EACH OTHER ON PARADIS.

KILLING EIGHTY PERCENT OF HUMANITY.

IT MUST HAVE HURT...

YOU'VE BEEN ALL ALONE SINCE THEN...

...WAS THE FUTURE YOU SAW AT THE MEDAL CEREMONY...

THAT...

SO...

I HAD TO DO IT...

THE FOUNDER'S POWER HAS MADE IT SO THAT THERE'S NO PAST OR FUTURE... IT ALL EXISTS AT ONCE.

ARMIN...

MY HEAD'S... GOTTEN ALL MESSED UP...

I WAS!

SO YOU WEREN'T LISTENING AFTER ALL...

...I DID.

DID YOU JUST SAY MIKASA?

HUH?

ONLY YMIR KNOWS THAT ONE...

WELL...

WHY MIKASA...?

AS FOR ME...

...EVEN I STILL DON'T KNOW...

..WHAT MIKASA WILL DO.

BUT... I KNEW SHE WAS IN AGONY AS SHE YEARNED FOR FREEDOM.

I CAN'T CLAIM TO UNDERSTAND THE DEPTHS OF YMIR'S HEART.

...SHE SOUGHT SOMEONE WHO'D RELEASE HER FROM THE AGONY OF HER LOVE.

FOR TWO THOU-SAND YEARS...

THEN, THAT SOMEONE APPEARED.

IT WAS MIKASA.

...

...SHE CONTINUED TO OBEY HIM.

BUT EVEN WHEN SHE ATTAINED GOD-LIKE POWERS...

HE'D BURNED HER HOMETOWN, KILLED HER PARENTS... AND PULLED OUT HER TONGUE.

RIGHT...

I COULDN'T BELIEVE IT, BUT...

...I FELT SOMETHING.

WHEN WE TOUCHED IN THE PATHS...

...COULD HAVE CAUSED HER TO DO THAT...?

WHAT...

THE FOUNDER, YMIR...

...LOVED KING FRITZ.

THAT'S WHAT BOUND HER FOR OVER TWO THOUSAND YEARS.

...WHAT?

...

SO THIS...

...IS BURN- ING WATER.

IT REALLY IS FLOWING LIKE A RIVER...

YOU SAID THAT THE POWER OF THE TITANS CONTINUES TO EXIST BECAUSE YMIR HAS BEEN OBEYING KING FRITZ FOR 2,000 YEARS...

...HM?

...WHERE DID I LEAVE OFF?

...

WAS THIS...

...ALL FOR OUR SAKE?

...REALLY NEED TO GO THIS FAR?

DID YOU...

LET'S TALK AS WE WALK.

WHERE WE WANTED TO GO.

WHERE ARE YOU...?

...ABOUT OUR FOUNDER, YMIR.

HUH?

THEY WON'T BE ABLE TO RETALIATE IMMEDIATELY.

WE'RE SUPPOSED TO PROTECT PARADIS FROM REPRISAL FROM HUMANITY OUTSIDE THE WALLS?

...SO YOU WANT US TO BE LIKE THE TYBUR FAMILY AFTER THE GREAT TITAN WAR?

THEY'LL LOSE THE CAPACITY TO WAGE WAR.

THE RUMBLING WILL KILL EIGHTY PERCENT OF HUMANITY.

...THAT'S RIGHT.

...AND MAKE US INTO HEROES WHO SAVED HUMANITY FROM EXTINCTION BY HUNTING YOU DOWN?

IT WAS ALL...

...TO PUSH US AWAY FROM YOU...

YOU TURNED YOUR BACKS ON PARADIS IN SPITE OF BEING "ISLAND DEVILS" TO STAND ON THE SIDE OF HUMANITY TO THE END.

HOW COULD YOU NOT BE SEEN AS SAVIORS BY EVERY SURVIVING HUMAN BEING?

YOU'D BECOME THE MOST RESPECTED PEOPLE IN THIS WORLD.

WHY?

WAS KNEEING ME THAT IMPORTANT?

BUT DID YOU REALLY HAVE TO BEAT ME TO A PULP..?

HEY, I GET IT... YOU DID IT FOR THE SAKE OF THE FUTURE YOU SAW USING THE ATTACK TITAN'S POWER.

...SORRY.

EVEN I FOUND MYSELF WONDERING WHAT I WAS DOING... I JUST LET THE MOMENT TAKE OVER... REALLY.

I WAS SO DESPERATE TO PUSH YOU ALL AWAY...

Final Episode: Toward the Tree on That Hill

ALL THAT NONSENSE YOU SPEWED HURT HER...

YOU SHOULD BE SAYING THAT TO MIKASA, NOT ME.

YEAH...

YOU'RE RIGHT.

SO FORGET ABOUT ME.

BE FREE...

YOU HAVE A LONG LIFE AHEAD OF YOU...

MIKASA.

PLEASE...

FORGET ABOUT ME.

...YES.

I'M SOR-RY.

I KNOW I PROMISED I WOULDN'T BRING THIS UP...

THROW THIS SCARF OUT ONCE I'M DEAD...

...WILL YOU MAKE ME ONE MORE PROMISE?

...IS LOOKING ALL OVER FOR US RIGHT NOW.

I BET ARMIN...

RUNNING AWAY IS THE ONLY WAY FOR ANYONE TO SURVIVE...

SO WHY NOT CHOOSE...

AND I COULDN'T DESTROY ALL OF HUMANITY OUTSIDE THE WALLS...

...AND CONTINUE THAT ENDLESS SLAUGHTER.

...COULDN'T SEND HISTORIA TO HELL...

I...

JUST THE TWO OF US?

...WHERE NOBODY ELSE IS AROUND...

...TO LIVE THE FOUR YEARS I HAVE LEFT IN PEACE AND QUIET...

...WHO ASKED ME THAT?

...YOU...

MIKASA. WASN'T IT...

MIKASA...

WHY... ARE YOU CRYING?

...HUH?

...SUDDENLY WASN'T SURE I BELONGED HERE...

I...

I WONDER WHY...

WHEN DID I FALL ASLEEP..?

LET'S JUST TAKE IT EASY FOR THE REST OF TODAY.

I MANAGED TO CATCH A BIG FISH, AFTER ALL...

I FEEL LIKE...

...I JUST HAD A LONG DREAM.

YOU MUST'VE BEEN EXHAUSTED...

MI-KA-SA.

WAKE UP.

YOU'LL CATCH A COLD.

HUH?

...I...

...EREN?

...I
WANT
TO GO
HOME.

I JUST...

...WANT TO
GO BACK...

...HOME...

THERE'S NO TELL-ING WHAT COULD HAPPEN!!

YOU CAN'T LET THAT SHINING THING COME IN CONTACT WITH EREN!

...OH NO.

THAT THING...

...EVEN START THE RUMBLING AGAIN...

IT MIGHT...

WE NEED TO GO...

...HOW DO WE KILL SOMETHING THAT SURVIVED THAT EXPLO-SION JUST NOW?

WE'VE GOTTA KILL THAT SHINING THING!!

THIS NIGHTMARE WON'T END UNTIL WE TAKE HIM DOWN...

YOU UNDER-STAND BY NOW, RIGHT...?

...FOR EREN.

...AND COLT'S, TOO.

I'M COM-PLETING MY MISSION...

I STILL HAVE ONE FINAL JOB.

FATHER.

...IT CAN'T BE...

I'VE ALWAYS HATED YOU.

MIKASA.

THAT...

...CAN'T BE OUR LAST...

URGH...

ARE YOU OKAY ?!

SIS!

AGH...

ALL THOSE BONES EXPLODED!!

...WHAT HAPPENED...?!

PLEASE HELP ME.

AFTER ALL THE KILLING I'VE DONE...

I SUPPOSE...

...THAT'S TOO MUCH TO ASK.

...WHAT A BEAUTIFUL DAY IT IS.

...I WISH I HAD SEEN IT EARLIER.

EVERY ELDIAN IS CONNECTED TO ONE ANOTHER BY THE PATHS.

I THINK...

...IT'S BECAUSE THE FOUNDER, YMIR, WANTED TO BE CONNECTED.

BECAUSE SHE WANTS SOMETHING FROM US...

BER-TOLT...

MISTER KSAVER.

WHAT?!

...?!

SNAP

PORCO!!

MARCEL!!

WHA ?!

GALLIARD!!

BOOM

BERTOLT...

BUT...

YOU'RE RIGHT...

IT DOESN'T MEAN A THING...

I...

...WOULD HAVE BEEN HAPPY PLAYING CATCH FOREVER.

...THAT...

...MIGHT ACTUALLY BE PRECIOUS...

...THESE TRIVIAL MOMENTS...

THAT...

WHY IS THAT...

...

IT WAS BURIED IN THE SAND...

THIS...?

...EVEN IF THERE'S NO NEED FOR SOMETHING LIKE THIS IN ORDER TO MULTIPLY...

BUT... TO MY EYES...

WHO KNOWS...

...IT'S STILL INCREDIBLY PRECIOUS.

I THOUGHT THE SAME THING LATER, READING A BOOK ON A RAINY DAY.

AND WHEN I GAVE A SQUIRREL SOME NUTS, AND IT ATE THEM.

AND WHEN WE WALKED AROUND THE MARKET.

...IT CAME TO ME AGAIN.

IS THE CONTINUED EXISTENCE OF YOUR SPECIES REALLY THAT IMPORTANT TO YOU?

YOU STILL SEEK TO MULTIPLY?

WELL...

A FEAR BORN OF LIFE-SUSTAINING FUNCTIONS THAT ARE COMPLETELY WITHOUT MEANING AND...

...ARE THE PITIFUL DEATH THROES OF LIFE FORMS CONTROLLED BY FEAR.

ONE MIGHT SAY WHAT WE'RE WITNESS-ING...

WHAT WE'RE DOING IS **FIGHTING** FEAR!!

BECAUSE WE CAN STILL SAVE SO MANY PEOPLE FROM TERROR...!!

MY FRIENDS... THEY'RE FIGHTING RIGHT NOW!!

YOU KNOW THAT TO LIVE...

...MEANS TO ONE DAY DIE, DON'T YOU?

AND WOULD IT BE SO WRONG TO LOSE THAT FIGHT?

Episode 137: Titans

HELLO.

MIS-
TER
ZEKE.

EREN'S
FRIEND.

HELLO
...

SO, YMIR
ATE YOU
TOO...?

...I'M SUPPOSED TO BE IN A TITAN'S MOUTH RIGHT NOW.

SO WHY DO I KNOW WHAT EVERYONE'S DOING...?

...BECAUSE ALL ELDIANS ARE CONNECTED VIA THESE PATHS?

BUT THAT MEANS...

THINK!!

THERE MIGHT BE... SOMETHING I CAN DO HERE.

YEAH.

THINK.

ZSSK

THE OKAPI...

...OH NO.

THEY'LL KILL YOU IN NO TIME!!

YOU CAN'T GO OFF ON YOUR OWN LIKE THAT!!

ANNIE!!

Episode 135: The Battle of Heaven and Earth

ATTACK ON TITAN

34

HAJIME ISAYAMA